What a Shower!

Written by Ben Farrell
Illustrated by Ken Spengler

HARCOURT BRACE & COMPANY

Orlando   Atlanta   Austin   Boston   San Francisco   Chicago   Dallas   New York
Toronto   London

The boy jumps in.

The girl jumps in.

The bird jumps in.

The cat jumps in.

The dog jumps in.

What a shower!